SOMETHING TO SING ABOUT

SONG LYRICS TO ENCOURAGE AND INSPIRE

BY JIM COLLINS

Contents

Foreword

Words are made of letters of hope.

Jim Collins and I grew up together, finding a common interest in words and music. Although to be fair in the early days Jim took sole credit for the music due to my very limited use of a tambourine! In our teens we encountered our individual faiths and again it was music, in the form of a 6th form rock band that united us. Since then we have gone our separate geographical ways but as all good friends do, we immediately reunite regardless of time or circumstance.

Today, I have the pleasure and responsibility of running one of the worlds largest academic publishers, something that would have seemed entirely fanciful in my younger years.

So in many ways it is words that still play an important role in my everyday life. It is of course accepted that in written and increasingly in electronic form, words are the tools and foundation of knowledge, education and communication.

They are more than just a random collection of letters; they are formed to express the emotion, the truth, the facts that are in our hearts and minds. In academia these words are sometimes long and complicated, preening themselves to prove their superiority, but for me the simplicity of succinct sentences win the argument every time.

Words composed in verse and set to music seem somehow to linger longer in the memory, and this brings me back to the reason for this book, which allows you to share in the word craft that has inspired Jim over the last thirty plus years to write songs that express the walk of faith that he has consistently and faithfully walked.

Together we used to sing his songs to small chapels, gatherings, and house groups, something that he has continued to do diligently since moving to Devon. Never to impress, only to impart his faith and his love of Christ.

Recovering from a serious illness recently, I found myself remembering lines from his songs like 'I want to say I'm sorry Lord for the times I've let you down' and encouraged that there is joy to be found when all around seems dark. So I would challenge you to find pleasure and meaning from the words and meaning contained in this book. You may just wish to ponder, or perhaps write your own music to accompany the words, or be inspired to write down your own heartfelt compositions.

The success of any writing should never be judged on the size of the audience but on the impact to any single individual. I do hope that the words of life in this book have the impact on you that they have always had on me.

Roger Horton, CEO Taylor & Francis Group

Introduction

It was back in 1974 (when I was nearing the age of eighteen) that I was invited to join my first band "Exodus" comprising of three guitarists, bass player and drummer. We did cover songs from *The Who, Free, Simon and Garfunkel* and *The Beatles* to name a few. We also played a selection of Christian message songs. My time with Exodus gave me confidence in performing in public.

I had written many poems as a young boy, and this led me to writing some of my own words to the song *"Light my fire"* by The Doors. The chorus read *"Come on Jesus light my way, turn me to the Christian way, help me make it last each day."* I wasn't a Christian when I wrote those lyrics – but "Exodus" was the means that God used to draw me to himself.

I didn't realise at the time; that those song words were a prayer to God which He answered. He did "turn me to the Christian way!"

The "head knowledge" that I had built up about God from attending Sunday School and Church Services over many years; became "real and life changing" to me, when I asked Jesus to come into my life, sought His forgiveness for my sinfulness and His help to enable me to live life His way.

As I've walked with God in my journey of life, He has never forsaken me. Through good and difficult times, joy and sadness, celebration and disappointment, He has continued to put a new song in my heart.

"*Something To Sing About*" is a compilation of 40 songs that I have written over the last 40 years. The *Something to sing about* is the "greatest" thing I could sing about – the Good News that God offers each of us a fresh start in life, the promise of new and abundant life each day and the certain hope of eternal life in Him.

I hope this book will be a helpful devotional to individuals – a resource for corporate reflection and prayer – and some inspiration for those who would like to use the words with their own melodies.

At the back of the book is a section called "*Between the lines*" which gives a short comment or thought about the theme of each song. As you read this book may God put His new song into your heart.

Jim Collins

I want to sing a song

I want to sing a song that glorifies your Name
I want to follow You – and live for You each day
When I see your work in me –
That only You could change
When I'm feeling low – I know you're there
You will bring me through – life's darkest hour
O Loving Lord – You are the One who cares

I want to sing a song that glorifies your Name
I want to lift my heart – and praise You Lord always
When I feel your love for me –
And see the price You paid
You are my Lord – You are my King
You're concerned in everything
O Loving Lord – to You my praise I bring

I want to sing a song that glorifies your Name

To love me and forgive – is why You came.

In You – my life is so complete

You came to make me whole

Almighty God You live in me

Giving strength and victory

O Loving Lord, like You I want to be

Shout with joy to God, all the earth!

Sing to the glory of His Name;

Offer Him glory and praise!

(Psalm 66:2)

In You Jesus

It is in You Jesus – I know love beyond compare
It is in You Jesus – You give help when I despair
I find light that shines through darkness –
And hope in the midst of fear
And it's all in You Jesus – I know you're always there

It is in You Jesus – I have a peace that's ever sure
It is in You Jesus, my life is now secure
You're a friend, my Lord and Saviour
You are just in all You do
And I can't live without You – I give my thanks to You

Chorus

I want to praise with all the love in my heart
It's in You O Lord – I rejoice
I give you praise – for your riches in grace
That You bestow on my life

It is in You Jesus – love and forgiveness flow

It is in You Jesus – all we need to know

I feel your mercy and compassion

As I bow before your throne

And it's all in You Jesus – I worship You alone

Chorus

> But I trust in You O LORD;
> I say, "You are my God."
> My times are in your hands…
> (Psalm 31:14-15a)

Only You

Only You – could know the way that I'm feeling

Only You – can feel my pain inside

Only You – know without me saying

Only You – know all the reasons why

Only You – surround me while I'm sleeping

Only You – know the reasons when I cry

Only You – give the breath for living

Only You – hold all things in my life

Chorus

Your love has always been around me

Long before my life began

And your thoughts to me are unending

For You know the way that I am

Only You – can give hope for the future

Only You – know me through and through

Only You – can make a life worth living

Only You – in everything I do

Chorus

Your love has always been around me

Long before my life began

And your thoughts to me are unending

For You know the way that I am

"How precious to me
are your thoughts, O God!
How vast is the sum of them!
(Psalm 139:17)

Jesus – light of the world

Chorus

Jesus the Light of the world
His love will shine down, when there's darkness all around
He will never leave you on your own
His light upon me – His light upon you
Jesus the Light of the world

When the clouds in life have come –
And they've hidden out the sun
And the road that lies ahead just isn't clear
There's a rainbow in the sky – to help us to rely
On the One who makes the storms all disappear

Chorus

If you're sad and in despair –

And your heart is full of fear

And the peace you're searching for cannot be found

There's a light that's shining through –

As you trust in all you do

To the One who puts your feet on solid ground

Chorus

Jesus said, "I am the light of the world. Whoever follows me will never walk in darkness, but will have the light of life."
(John 8:12)

Two edged sword

In your word – I have read – all the things You require
Make it real – in my heart – make it my one desire
That I heed what I hear – and then do what You say
May I live – in your love – and your promises each day

I can see – through the dark – when I live in your light
When my faith – is in You – I walk no longer by sight
But by trust – in You God – You are higher than I
By your words – I stand firm – for in them I rely

Chorus

Just like a shining two edged sword
Your words cut deep in my heart
Making me see – that I must believe
What You say – must come to pass

Your Word of so old – and yet for today
I know will never fade away
When I believe what You say – then I will see
My hopes become reality.

In my life – I can know – all my times in your care
When alone – or afraid, then with You I can share
And you'll give – me a word – and I know that it's true
As it dwells – in my mind – then the problem is through

Chorus

"You are my refuge and my shield;
I have put my hope in your word."
(Psalm 119:114)

All things work together for good

Chorus

All things work together for good –
To those who love your name.
And those who put their trust in You –
Will never be ashamed

And I will sing – of all that You have done
O Jesus You have come –
To give us life and peace –
And share with us your love
And I will praise – whatever comes my way
Whatever men may say
In you I find the grace – to meet my every need

Chorus

And to You – I sing a brand new song
For You have made me strong
To face each day at peace –
Where fear had once been known

I rejoice – in the knowledge of You Lord
Believing in your Word
That never fails – and won't ever pass away

Chorus into

Middle

Greater are You in me – than he, that's in the world
Every knee will bow to You
And tongue confess you're Lord!

"The Lord works out everything
for His own ends" ...
(Psalm 16:4a)

Faith in your great faithfulness

When I swim against the tide – when I walk into the wind
When I need a place to hide – and the ice I'm on is thin
When I can't see beyond the mist – I can only feel the rain
But I know that You are here – so I turn to You again

Chorus

I put my trust in You – for You are ever true
I put my faith – in your great faithfulness
I rest my life in You – for You will pull me through
I will know your grace – unending

When I feel the desert heat –
When I'm searching for the shade
And I walk with aching feet – and stumble on the way
When tears are in my eyes – and my heart is full of fear
I will not give up – for I know that You are near.

Chorus

Middle

Your love – Your peace – Your Word – Is perfect
Your love – Your peace – Your Word – Is perfect

Chorus to end

When I am afraid, I will trust in You.

(Psalm 56:3)

God is my strength

God is my strength – my shield and tower
A present help in life's dark hour
Unfailing love – unending grace
Pours from His heart and strengthens faith
Lord of all life – King of all days
Sovereign Lord – worthy of praise
My hiding place – and security
God is my rock – eternally

Jesus; God's Son – to this world came
Forgives my sin – and takes my shame
The sinner's friend – Shepherd and Guide
Draws close in love – walks by my side
Christ of the Cross – the vict'ry won
Salvation free – and death is gone
Surpassing peace – astounding love
Lord of my life – my Advocate.

Jesus is Lord – Light of the world

God in the flesh – the Living Word

Awesome in power – and majesty

Creator God – alive in me

Jesus; the Way – the Truth and Life

Deliverer – from fear and strife

My joy on earth – my hope to come

King of my heart – the risen One

"Sing for joy to God our strength"…

(Psalm 81:1a)

Teach us to pray

Lord we bring our prayers to You
And ask that you'll be pleased to do
The things we ask –
Believing in your name.

Chorus

Teach us to pray O Lord – the things upon your heart
Teach us to pray O Lord – To wait upon your word.

Lord we ask that You will show
The words to speak – the way to go
So in everything –
We glorify your name

Chorus

Lord we come to You in need
On our behalf – You intercede
You're a loving God –
Who hears us when we call

Chorus

"Do not be anxious about anything,
but in everything, by prayer and petition,
with thanksgiving, present your
requests to God."
(Philippians 4:6)

God of my life

Lord I don't know what to do
But my eyes are on You
For You are the strength within me
I will wait on You

At times – words don't come when I pray
But my mind – is on You
Just to know your presence each day
Is all I – need to know

Chorus

For You are the God of my life
You are the King of all Kings
You are the Lord of all heaven and earth
To You all creation sings

Seeking the way I should turn

I reach out to You

You are all knowing and true

I will trust in You

Chorus

Jesus said…

"I have come that they may have life,

and have it to the full."

(John 10:10)

Worthy of our praise

Jesus you're the One – we come and worship

For You alone are worthy of our praise

Speak your word – into our situations

To change our hearts and minds – to know your ways

Lord to You – our hands we raise

For You are worthy of our praise

Holy Spirit come and move among us

So Jesus has all glory to His Name

Reveal to us your will, and greater purpose

So nothing of ourselves gets in the way

Lord to You – our hands we raise

For You are worthy of our praise

Lord we come to You in adoration
Laying all we have down at your feet
Lord we come to You for restoration
Knowing You will meet our every need
Lord to You, we bow our knee
In You, we have the victory

Great is the Lord
and most worthy of praise
His greatness no-one can fathom
(Psalm 145:3)

You give yourself to me

When the wind is blowing strong and endless
And I sense the surging of the sea
It reminds me Lord – that you're astounding
When I'm weak – You put your strength in me

Chorus

You show your kindness – without measure
Grace and power – for every need
Love and mercy – priceless treasure
Lord – You give yourself to me

(Repeat chorus)

When the storms may appear – never ending
You won't allow any more than I can take
When doubts feel stronger – than believing
And the world around my feet may shake

Chorus

Middle

Lord You give yourself – You give yourself
You give yourself to me
Lord You give yourself – You give yourself
You give yourself to me

"They cried to You and were saved;
In You they trusted
and were not disappointed."
(Psalm 22:5)

Maker of heaven and earth

Chorus

I lift my eyes – up to the hills

Where does my help come from?

My help comes – from the Lord

Maker of Heaven and Earth – Maker of Heaven and Earth

He will not let – your foot slip away

He watches over you

His eyes upon you – He never sleeps

Keeping you – night and day

Chorus

I lift my eyes – up to the hills

Where does my help come from?

My help comes – from the Lord

Maker of Heaven and Earth

Maker of Heaven and Earth

He is the Lord – at your right hand

He will keep you secure

When coming in – or going out

Both now and evermore

Chorus

"Come; let us bow down in worship,
Let us kneel before the LORD
our Maker."
(Psalm 95:6)

This is what the Lord says

This is what the Lord says – this is what the Lord says
This is what the Lord says – to you

Let not the wise man – boast of his wisdom
Or the strong man – boast of his strength
Or the rich man – boast of his riches
But let him who boasts – boast about this

Chorus

He is the King of kindness – Judge of all justice
Reigns in righteousness – on earth
He is the King of kindness – Judge of all justice
Reigns in righteousness on earth

Hear to what the Lord says – hear to what the Lord says
Hear to what the Lord says – to you

God made the earth – by His great power
And by wisdom – founded the world
Through understanding – stretched out the heavens
When He thunders – the waters in the heavens roar
So let him who boasts – boast in the Lord

Chorus

Bridge

I delight in these – I delight in these
I delight in these – declares the Lord – *(Repeat)*

End:

Do you understand and know Me? *(Repeat to fade)*

"My tongue will speak of your
righteousness and of your
praises all day long."
(Psalm 35:28)

I want to say I'm sorry Lord

I want to say I'm sorry Lord –
For the times I've let You down
But You set me back – along the way
And I wear the Victors crown
I thank You Lord for helping me
Through times which have seemed bad
I thank You for your love to me – and everything I have

I want to say I'm sorry Lord –
When I just don't fear your Name
If the road is rough – You come to me
With a love that will remain.
You offer me your hand
And You guide me on my way
I thank You and I praise You Lord –
'Cos I need You every day

Chorus

You're like the morning sunshine –

When You guide me in the light

You're the Ruler King of Justice – showing me what's right

You speak to me – watch over me – You never let me fall

You listen and you're teaching me –

And You answer when I call

I want to say I'm sorry Lord – When I go my selfish way

But I know – that you've forgiven me –

Such grace I can't explain

I really am so glad O Lord – that You showed yourself to me

For once I was a prisoner – but now you've set me free.

"Who can discern his errors?
Forgive my hidden faults."
(Psalm 19:12)

Love's greatest story (Easter Song)

Above His head – they wrote the charge
Jesus Christ – King of the Jews
In His hands – He bore the scars
Of His endless love for you
There is mercy and forgiveness
You can have a brand new start
You can know Love's greatest story in your heart

Chorus

And it Love's greatest story
That the King of all the world should die for me
Yes – it's Love's greatest story
Turned the darkness and the pain to victory

Upon the cross – He bled and died
A sacrifice – for every sin
And His arms – are open wide
To embrace – and to receive
There is kindness and compassion
New life He will impart
You can know Love's greatest story in your heart

Chorus – into final chorus

And it Love's greatest story
That the King of all the world should die for me
And He rose from death in glory
Turned the darkness and the pain to victory

"Greater love has no-one than this,
that one lay down His life
for His friends."
(John 15:13)

Everyone needs Jesus

How are you today – are you empty deep inside?

Can you see across life's river–

But can't reach the other side?

Are you stumbling on life's mountains –

Or sinking in the sea?

Everyone needs Jesus – and that means you and me

You say you're always trying –

On your own to make it through

You think that life will place itself –

Around the things you do

But I tell you without Jesus – you can't make it on your own

For we were all made for Him – to glorify His name

Chorus

Everyone needs Jesus – to guide in all they do

A friend who always listens – His promises are true

A love that's never ending – and peace within your mind

To know your sins forgiven – to have eternal life

Everyone needs Jesus.

Do you feel the joy inside – from knowing Christ as Lord?

Do you know your needs supplied – by trusting in His word?

Have you felt His healing hand –

When your strength has gone away?

But if Jesus is your Lord – then you only have to pray

Everyone needs Jesus – He's coming back one day

And if you never knew Him – there'll be no other way

He will call His servants to Him – to live for evermore

He's calling out to you right now – just open up the door

Everyone needs Jesus!

And everyone who calls on the name
of the Lord will be saved."
(Acts 2:21)

Message to you

You can live for yourself –
You can say, that you know what is right.
You can do what you please – but it only leads to strife
You can try on your own – to make life as good as can be
But if you can't find time for God – you just won't see

You can turn your back – and walk in the opposite way
But the road of life will end for you one day
Then where will you go – and what will your answer be?
When Jesus asks "Did you follow Me?"

Chorus

He just wants to get His message to you
He wants to be in all that you do
He just wants to get His message to you
"I love you."

You can know Him now – as you ask His forgiveness on you

The old ways of your life – are changed for new

As you trust in the Lord – He will keep your mind at peace

The joy that Jesus gives – will never cease

Chorus to end

> Jesus said "Greater love has no-one than this, that one lay down his life for his friends. You are my friends if you do what I command."
> (John 15:13-14)

Forgiveness

Could you love someone – who speaks against you?
Can you love your neighbour as yourself?
Are you judged for doing wrong –
When you're really in the right?
Could you love a wicked man who's needing help?

Can you stand to face someone who mocks your Saviour?
And speak alone for Him – when no one cares?
Forgive a person's ways – when they're opposite to yours
Speak the word "Forgiveness" in their ears.

Chorus

For it's in Jesus – we know forgiveness
Our every weakness He knows
He comes to cleanse us – and help us –
So His love overflows
Forgive men their trespasses – as Jesus forgives us.
Forgive them by your loving – and do not be their judge

Could you give a helping hand to one who hates you?

Could you go that extra mile to show you care?

Can you turn the other way – and just carry on the same?

Although your load at times is hard to bear

Chorus to end

"You are kind and forgiving, O Lord,
abounding in love to all who call to You."
(Psalm 86:5)

Open hands

You O Lord, have made me worthy
You lift me up – so I can I stand
You alone, have made me holy
I come to You with open hands

I just want to bring You glory
I bow in worship at your feet
I know You have – so much more for me
Forgive me when I don't receive

Chorus

I come with open hands – You come with open arms
I walk towards your love – You run to me.
I look to You O Lord – You see right into me
Before I even ask
You know what I need

Come and fill me – precious Jesus
Less of me – and more of You
Come anoint me – Holy Spirit of God
I receive You LORD

Chorus to end

I come with open hands – You come with open arms

I walk towards your love – You run to me.

I look to You O Lord – You see right into me

Before I even ask

You know what I need

> "I call to You, O Lord, every day;
> I spread out my hands to You."
> (Psalm 88:9b)

King Jesus

I'm a friend of Jesus Christ
I'm a child of the living God
I'm a servant of the King
I am loved by the risen Lord

Chorus

King Jesus – King Jesus
Reign – deep in my heart
King Jesus – King Jesus
Sovereign Lord over all

I'm called by your Holy Name
And a witness to your love
Set apart to do your works
Restored by your life and power

Chorus

I am strong in your Spirit's power
I'm secure in your endless grace
I am healed by your loving touch
And I rest in your embrace

Chorus and verse 1 to end

"For the LORD is the great God,
the great King above all gods."
(Psalm 95:3)

The puzzle jig (Children's Song)

Chorus

There's a God shaped hole within my heart

That only Jesus can fill

Whatever people say – whatever comes my way

Nothing is ever as "brill"

As knowing – Jesus

As loving – Jesus

As serving – Jesus – with all your heart

Just like a jigsaw – life is a puzzle

Just don't know where to start

Let's turn to Jesus – and He will help us

When we pray and ask

Chorus

With lots of pieces, and many places –
Every day – to go
We will seek Jesus – and He will lead us
And show us what to do

Chorus to end

"For this God is our God
for ever and ever;
He will be our guide even to the end."
(Psalm 48:14)

What would Jesus do? (Children's Song)

Chorus

What would Jesus do?

I will do what's right – and say what's true

I will read His word – then I will know

Know what Jesus would do

What would Jesus do?

Forgive the one – who speaks against you

Go to the one – who needs helping through

That's what Jesus would do

In the times when I am tempted – to do just as I please

I will call upon the Lord who rescues me

And His strength will always keep me – my desire is to obey

I will always run to Him – not run away

Chorus

I want to follow Jesus – living for Him every day

In my thoughts – the things I do – and words I say

Every step and each direction – wherever it may go

My prayer will be – "What would Jesus do?"

Repeat chorus to end

"To do your will, O my God, is my desire;

your law is within my heart."

(Psalm 40:8)

24

I know a King who can (Children's Song)

I know a King – who can do all things
I know a King – who can move mountains
I know a King – who forgives sin
Jesus the King who can

Sovereign Lord over all – Maker of heaven and earth
You came into my life – You have given me worth

Chorus

You are the King – who can do all things…
You are the King who can
When I'm feeling unsure – and I can't see the way
I will cast all my cares – on You Lord and I'll pray

Chorus

Pray to the King – who can do all things…
Pray to the King who hears
When the doubts and the guilt –
Come and knock at my door!
I'll put my trust in You Lord – for I can be sure

Chorus

You are the King – who can do all things…
You are the King who can
I know that God is for me – and I have nothing to fear
As my heart sings your praise – I long to draw near

Chorus

Near to the King – who can do all things…
Near to the King who cares

> "For nothing is impossible with God."
> (Luke 1:37)

25

Follow Me (Children's Song)

Jesus walked along the shore of the lake of Galilee

Then He saw two brothers fishing –

Their nets upon the sea

Walking on He saw a boat

Inside were James and John

He asked them all to come with Him

They left and ran along – when He said

Chorus

"Follow Me – and I'll make you fishers of men"

And He said – "Follow Me –

Stop what you're doing and come"

So they left their fishing behind –

And walked with peace of mind

Following the teaching of Jesus – and His words

Many people on their way – said "Lord I will follow You

In every way – in all my life – just tell me what to do"

Then they said "Lord I won't be long –

I'll just finish what I must do"

But Jesus said "Leave it right away –

Come to Me now – we must go" – and He said

Chorus

"Teach me O Lord,
to follow your decrees;
Then I will keep them to the end."
(Psalm 119:33)

26

Baptise me (Baptismal Song)

I'm standing here today Lord for You
I heard your voice so clear what I must do
I'm going through these waters Lord
For I know that you've been too
I want to follow on – wherever You go

I know what lies ahead is your command
I'm reaching out to You – to take my hand
I recognise – I've died to self
I'm raised to life anew
So I can live your life – in all that I do

Chorus

Baptise me in this water Lord –
Baptise me with your power
Baptise me with your Spirit Lord – I need You every hour
Baptise me in this water Lord – baptise me with your fire
You promise this to those who follow You

I want to heed your word – for You are true

As I decrease – I will look more to You

I then will see – that in your strength

And nothing of my own

No longer me but You – my whole life through

Chorus to end

Jesus –
"He will baptise you with the
Holy Spirit and with fire."
(Matthew 3:11b)

27

Faithful God

You are a faithful God – throughout the generations
You are a faithful God – in all the things You do
And we give You our praise – and sing with adoration
Faithful God – Mighty Lord – we worship You

Build your Church O Lord – within our town and nation
We are trusting You – your promises are sure
Jesus our rock – strong and sure foundation
Faithful God – Mighty Lord – we worship You

Chorus

Move us on – move us out – in your love O Lord
In your kindness and humility
May our lives – be the touch – of your peace O Lord
In the places – You want us to be

You are gracious Lord – revealing your compassion
From an endless store – your riches shared with me
Your forgiving love – never fails to bring us through
Faithful God – Mighty Lord – we worship You

Chorus

Move us on – move us out – in your love O Lord
In your kindness and humility
May our lives – be the touch – of your peace O Lord
In the places – You want us to be

"For great is your love, reaching
to the heavens; your faithfulness
reaches to the skies."
(Psalm 57:10)

28

In our midst

Prayer Chorus

In our midst O Lord – may your Spirit be
In your love O Lord – set your people free

In your grace and favour – we seek your purity
Changed by You – to the people we should be

Prayer Chorus

In our midst O Lord – may your Spirit be
In your love O Lord – set your people free

In your care and presence – we place our every need
You will bless – as we walk righteously

Prayer Chorus

In our midst O Lord – may your Spirit be
In your love O Lord – set your people free

Ruler of the nations – LORD of everything

We lift our hands – in worship as we sing

Prayer Chorus

In our midst O Lord – may your Spirit be

In your love O Lord – set your people free

"For where two or three are gathered in My name, I am there in the midst of them."
(Matthew 18:20)

65

29

Strong love (Wedding Song)

Gracious is the Lord your God
He brought your lives together
And trusting in His every word
You'll know His love – forever.

Chorus

In His strong love – always seek to follow
In His presence – live for today
In His strong arms – rest your each tomorrow
In His strong love – For you

Living for the Lord your God
Serving Him – and each other
Sharing in His endless love
Will keep your hearts rejoicing

Chorus

Middle

And may the light of Jesus –

Guide your hearts so you will know

All the things that God has planned – for you to do

Faithful is the Lord your God

Always ready to pardon

Listening to His every word

Always there to rely on

Chorus to end

"How priceless is your unfailing love!"

(Psalm 36:7a)

30

The Holy Highway

The desert will rejoice – the parched land shout for joy
And all will see the splendour of the Lord
And the greatness of His power –
Will be a strength and tower
To the hands and knees that tremble when they're tired

Chorus

Tell all – who are dismayed – be strong don't be afraid
For God is coming now – in power to save
So tell all who are dismayed – be strong don't be afraid
From the hand of enemies – He will rescue

The deaf ears now can hear –
and the lame dance like the deer
And the blind eyes shall be opened – and will see
For in the desert they can go – for streams of water flow
Where the jackals use to live – the grass will grow

Chorus

There will be a Highway there –
and no sinner will come near
To the City of the LORD – where you will be
And the ransomed travel home – along that Holy Road
Where all sorrow, grief and sighing – flee away

Chorus

Tell all who are dismayed – be strong don't be afraid
For God is coming now – in power to save
So tell all who are dismayed – be strong don't be afraid
From the hand of enemies – He will rescue

"…say to those with fearful hearts,
Be strong, do not fear;
your God will come…"
(Isaiah 35:4a)

31

With all your heart

Chorus

Whatever the Lord tells you to do – Do it with all your heart
When you obey – without delay
Then a miracle – a mighty work can start

At a wedding down in Cana – Jesus gave a sign
He revealed His glory – as the water turned to wine
The master of the banquet – could not understand
But the servants who had heeded –
Rejoiced at His command

Chorus

Whatever the Lord tells you to do – Do it with all your heart
When you obey – without delay
Then a miracle – a mighty work can start

As the people followed Jesus – to the shores of Galilee

Thousands came before Him –

For the things that they had seen

A crowd of hungry people – were fed with fish and bread

When a little boy – gave all he had

And they did what Jesus said

Chorus

Whatever the Lord tells you to do – Do it with all your heart

When you obey – without delay

Then a miracle – a mighty work can start

Jesus' mother said to the servants
"Do whatever He tells you."
(John 2:5)

32

Where can I go?

Lord You have searched me – and You know all my ways
You know my sitting down – and rising too
You search out my path – you're acquainted with me
There's no word on my tongue – that You don't know

Chorus

Where can I go – from your Spirit Lord?
Where can I go – from your presence?
Where can I go – from your Spirit Lord?
Even darkness hides nothing from You

I was not hid from You – through the days that I was made
You really know my being through and through
Your thoughts to me are more –
Than the number of the sand
When I awake – I still would be with You

Chorus

Middle

If I ascend up into heaven – You are there

If I make my bed in Sheol – You are there

If I take the wings of morning – and dwell the deepest sea

Even there – shall your hand take hold on me

Final Chorus

There's nowhere to go – from your Spirit Lord

There's nowhere to go – from your presence

There's nowhere to go – from your Spirit Lord

Even darkness hides nothing from You

"You have made known to me
the path of life;
You fill me with joy in your presence,
with eternal pleasures at your right hand."
(Psalm 16:11)

33

Think (upon these things)

When doubts come down – and fears arise
Dark shadows falling all around
Don't despair – for God draws near
To bring His peace into your mind
Think – upon – these things

Chorus

Whatever things are noble – whatever things are true
Whatever things are lovely – whatever things are pure
Think on things admirable – whatever things are right
Everything of excellence – worthy of praise in His sight

Let every thought – be captive now
In obedience to the Lord
To His commands – delight and will
Be still and know that He is Lord
Think – upon – these things

Chorus

Whatever things are noble – whatever things are true

Whatever things are lovely – whatever things are pure

Think on things admirable – whatever things are right

Everything of excellence – worthy of praise in His sight

"…fix your thoughts on Jesus…"

(Hebrews 3:1)

34

Light on the horizon

When the clouds of life are floating low
And everything looks grey
And the winds are blowing hard on me
And I feel I've lost my way

But when I call to You – You come to me
You make the storms to cease
You walk out to me – on the troubled sea
And give to me your peace

Chorus

You are the light on the horizon
The dawning of a brand new day
The clouds above are passing me by
And You are on your way (to me)

In quietness and confidence
You give your strength to me
And nothing can contain your love
You give to me so free

In everything you're teaching me

To put my trust in you

I'm not alone – for You are here

To always pull me through

Chorus to end

"The true light that gives light
to every man
was coming into the world."
(John 1:9)

35

For You O Lord (Psalm 116)

Chorus

For You O Lord have delivered my soul

My eyes from tears – and my feet from falling

That I may walk – before You Lord

In the land of the living

I love You Lord – for You heard my voice

You heard me call out for mercy

You turned your ear – to the sound of my cry

Forever LORD – I will praise You

Chorus

When overcome – by trouble and strife

I will call upon – your Name O LORD

When I'm in need – You rescue me

Be at rest once more – O my soul

Middle

The Lord is gracious – The Lord is righteous
Our God is full of compassion
How can I repay – all His goodness to me?
I will lift up – the cup of salvation

So let's come dancing – let us come singing
Let's praise the Lord with our thanksgiving

Chorus to end

"I will sacrifice a thank-offering to You
and call on the name of the Lord."
(Psalm 116:17)

36

Thorn in the hay (Christmas Song)

There's a baby boy
Lying in a manger
See His mother's joy
As she holds those tiny hands

God is with us now
Baby and Creator
Here in David's Town
A Saviour has been born

Chorus

There's a thorn in the hay
That leads us to the way
Where love is shown – upon a cross of shame

Glory shone around
Angels appearing
Shepherds come and bow
To the King of all the World

Chorus

Thorns upon His head – Bearing all our sorrow

On the cross He bled – Taking all our sin

Chorus to end

> A Saviour has been born! This will be a
> sign to you: you will find a baby wrapped
> in strips of cloth and lying in a manger."
> (Luke 2:11-12)

37

Glory to God in the highest

(Christmas Song)

Chorus

Glory to God in the highest
Jesus the Lord is here
The King has come – to His people
Good News – and no more fear

He will be called – the Son of the Most High
Saviour of the world – Come to Israel
Immanuel – for God is with us now!

Chorus

Came to a world – so full of misery
People who were lost – have found their destiny
In Jesus – for God is with us now!

Chorus

He's the Mighty God – and the Prince of Peace
He will be great – His government increase
Immanuel – for God is with us now

Chorus to end

Glory to God in the highest

Jesus the Lord is here

The King has come – to His people

Good News – and no more fear

"The virgin will be with child and will give birth to a son, and they will call Him Immanuel" which means, "God with us" (Matthew 1:23)

38

Fully God and Fully Man

(Christmas Song)

Up to the royal town of David
Joseph and Mary made their way
God sent His Son to be our Saviour
On that first Christmas day

The little baby in the manger
Is the LORD – the great I AM
Full of grace – and truth and mercy
Fully God – and fully man

Chorus

His light has broken through the darkness
The love of God – to earth come down
Jesus – the Ruler of the nations
Fully God – and fully man

Shepherds watching from the hillside

Hear the news – that "Christ is here!"

Lifting up the broken hearted

Bringing peace – into our fear

Chorus

His light has broken through the darkness

The love of God – to earth come down

Jesus – the Ruler of the nations

Fully God – and fully man

The Word became flesh and lived for a
while among us."
(John 1:14a)

39

To the King who reigns

(Christmas Song)

Unto us a child is born
Unto us a Son is given
And the government shall be
On the shoulders of the King
And His Name is Wonderful
Counsellor and Mighty God
Eternal Father – Prince of Peace
And upholding righteousness

Chorus

To the King who reigns – I'll bow down
To the King who reigns – I'll bow down
To the King who saves – I will crown
I will crown Him – Lord of All

Unto us a child is born
Unto us a Son is given
And with justice He will reign
From that time forth and evermore

And my songs shall ever be

To the King of all the earth

Lay my life down at His feet

And bow in praise before His throne

Chorus to end

"The people walking in darkness have
seen a great light"…
(Isaiah 9:2)

40

The Magi's Song (Christmas Song)

When we came to Jerusalem
Many days had passed by then
Searching for the new-born King
For we had come to worship

Pre verse (Repeat twice)

Singing – Glory be – to God on High
And peace to earth from heaven

The Christ was born in Bethlehem
In the land of Judah
Out from there – will come our King
A Shepherd and a Ruler

Pre-verse

Middle

We have seen His star – shining from the heavens
We have seen His star – His glory filled our hearts
We have seen His light – dawning in our darkness
And we worship Christ the King

We laid our treasures at His feet
And bowed in adoration
Incense – gold and myrrh we gave
To the King of all Creation

Pre-verse to end

"When they saw the star,
they were overjoyed"
(Matthew 2:10)

Between The Lines

I want to sing a song

(1990) This is a personalised prayer-song that enabled me and others to express the desire that "God should have all the glory in all things."

Every skill and talent that we have is God given. He created us to be creative. When people comment and congratulate me on my abilities I can accept their appreciation, but the glory and praise always belongs to God. Each line of this song is addressed directly to the LORD, a heart to heart where we honour Him with our worship.

In You Jesus

These words came to me in 2000 when I was preparing and seeking God for an opportunity to serve as a Church Pastor.

There are dozens of verses in the Bible that remind us of our blessings, inheritance and identity that we have "In Christ." Everything we need is found in Him alone.

"...our sufficiency is from God." (2 Corinthians 3:5 NKJV)

Only You

This is my only song that does not mention God, Jesus or Lord but every word is directed to Him. It was inspired by the birth of our only precious daughter Sarah, in 1985. During one of those occasions when I'd tried everything to settle our baby and she was still crying and restless, I was reminded that when we are experiencing pain or distress – God is familiar with our suffering and it is impossible to count the vastness of His thoughts towards us. (Psalm 139:17-18) I played in a Band called "Known Aim" for 13 years and in October 1995, one of our members, Jackie, sadly passed away after a battle against cancer. We were asked to sing this song at her funeral. God gave us His strength and grace to do so.

Jesus – Light of the World

Jesus is the Light of the World but in His Sermon on the Mount He says to us "You are the light of the world." (Matthew 5:14) Like a city on a hill that cannot be hidden, our faith and our works for God must be evident for all to see. In June 1993 I sang this song (with Known Aim) in the Brixham Heritage Festival "Song Competition."

We were 1 of 8 finalists. We didn't win but it was a great opportunity to be able to share the gospel in words and music.

Two Edged Sword

This song has been one of my favourites (written in the early 80's) it is one of my "most sung" numbers. In Hebrews 4:12, God's Word the Bible, is described as being sharper than any double edged sword. It is living and active!

God makes His will and purposes known to us through His Word, and as we read the scriptures and become "doers of the word", we grow in our faith, and see God's promises come to pass in our lives.

All things work together for good

(1992) These lyrics speak about one of the greatest promises that God makes to us as His disciples. But it can also be one of the hardest to work through.

When life's problems hit you face on – when ill health, redundancy, bereavement or relationship breakdown strikes, it is not always clear initially, how God is going to work things out for the best for those who love Him. (Romans 8:28)

Keep trusting Him! God is working out His best purposes for us and through us.

Faith in your great faithfulness

(2008) These words use different elements of the weather (wind, ice, mist, rain and heat) to describe some of the difficulties we face in life.

Sometimes, when the storms in life hit us hard we can lose our focus. It's during these tough times that we need to remind ourselves that God is always faithful to His Word and promises. He is always with us. The chorus reminds us to call upon the LORD, who is ever true, ever faithful and pours out un-ending grace into our lives. "If we are faithless, He will remain faithful..." (2 Timothy 2:13)

God is my strength

Back in 2004 BBC Radio Devon held a Hymn writing competition. This was my entry. The hymn uses many of the Names and attributes of God.

"The name of the Lord is a strong tower; the righteous run to it and are safe." (Proverbs 18:10)

"Our help is in the name of the Lord, the Maker of heaven and earth." (Psalm 124:8) God will be to us, all that we need, as we follow and trust Him.

Teach us to pray

(1996) Taken from Luke 11:1 – the chorus is a prayer – asking Jesus to help us to pray. Prayer is the great privilege we have to enter into the presence of God and grow in our relationship with Jesus.

We share the things on our heart and God shares what's on His heart with us as we wait and listen. Each time we talk to God He wants to reply in some way. It may not always be with immediate answers or in ways that we expect but He will always do something when we pray.

One of the best things we can do is to encourage and enable others to pray, seek and hear from God as we continue to learn how to pray.

God of my life

Near the end of an evening sermon in 2001 the preacher concluded his sermon by saying "Lord; we don't know what to do but our eyes are on You." Noting the rhyming words and an important theme – this song soon followed. It expresses that when we don't know how to pray or understand what's going on, God's presence is enough.

I chose this song for my Induction Service when I became a Lay Pastor of a local Church in 2002; to express my desire to look to, wait upon, and trust in the God of my life.

Worthy of our praise

In the late 80's I was busy playing with a band and doing regular preaching in several Churches. Smaller congregations were always appreciative when I came along with my guitar. This song was taught and shared at several Churches to encourage them to sing a new song to the Lord.

On some occasions, I would share a song as a solo, or sing the verse solo and teach the congregation the chorus, for them to join in. Today; when most Church Services have mostly congregational (participation) singing, I still sense there is great blessing in solo or band compositions that are shared to be listened to. It's what I used to call "ministry in song" (or preaching to music!).

You give yourself to me

(2003) I was taking a study week at Lee Abbey in North Devon and one cool and windy afternoon I took a stroll down to the private beach within the grounds and watched the waves.

Inspired by the surging sea I was reminded of God's awesome power, and how He gives of himself to us in His strength, kindness, love, mercy and grace.

Maker of Heaven and Earth

(2006) Psalm 121 reminds us to lift our eyes to the Lord. The One who made heaven and earth and holds it all in place is the One who sends us help when we call upon His Name.

The best words we can sing about, are the scriptures; reminding us of God's commands, His characteristics and promises.

In 1985 I sent a demo of some of my songs to a recording company. They replied saying "…the lyrics are rather obvious, and we don't feel that we are able to use the songs commercially." However God continued to use the songs He had put on my heart. One of the greatest privileges for sharing the gospel in song came from the many occasions we had to sing them to inmates in Dartmoor and Channings Wood Prison.

This is what the Lord says

(2007) This song is based on Jeremiah's words. (Jeremiah 9:23 / 10:12-13) and is one of the longest songs I have composed.

The chorus and end line of this song bring together the great hope we have, that we can understand and know the Lord God who is the King of all kindness and the Judge of all justice.

I want to say I'm sorry Lord

I wrote this song (in the late 70's) when I was young in my Christian faith. It spoke from a saddened heart that recognised the times when I let God down and displeased Him, when I went my way instead of His.

As the years have passed by; Jesus has continued to lift me up, after each time I have fallen. That's why I'm still standing for Him today, guitar in hand and a song in my heart.

"Praise the Lord, O my soul, and forget not all His benefits. He forgives all my sins and heals all my diseases; He redeems my life from the pit and crowns me with love and compassion." (Psalm 103:2-4)

Loves greatest story

In 2001 I commenced full time Church ministry. That year, I ordered some Easter service invitation material. "Loves greatest story" were the words on the front of the invite that we distributed. I often find that a few words for a title, theme or chorus line triggers the rest of the song.

The greatest love story ever: is that Jesus the Son of God and King of all the world, was prepared to die for the sins of each one of us and in receiving His forgiveness we can know friendship and fellowship with our Father in Heaven.

Everyone needs Jesus

(1982) I sang this song at a good number of Open Air Services. It asks six questions of the listener and speaks of our attempts to find purpose in life. When we sing our Christian lyric songs outside of the four walls of our Churches; "worship becomes witness". Our love for God is made known. I still sense there is great opportunity to be taken by encouraging and releasing more Church worship bands and Christian song artists into singing about the Good News of Jesus in the streets, and at other outdoor social gatherings.

Message to you

(1988) This song is another one of my favourites that I shared at Open Air Services.

It looks at how life may look when people don't acknowledge God, leading into a chorus that speaks about one of the greatest messages and promises that God gives to us in His Word that we can know and experience personally – the great love and saving power of God.

"For God so loved the world that He gave His one and only Son, that whoever believes in Him shall not perish but have eternal life." (John 3:16)

Forgiveness

The questions posed in this song address situations about our relationships with others where we need to respond with forgiveness. The apostle Paul instructs us to "Bear with each other and forgive whatever grievances you may have against one another. Forgive as the Lord forgave you." (Colossians 3:13)

Some aspects of forgiveness will take time to work through but we must also understand that forgiveness is a choice of our will. We must choose to forgive; every time, someone offends, hurts or sins against us. The result is: we will know inner peace and be free from the constant pain of bitterness, anger and resentment that un-forgiveness brings.

Open hands

Written in 2000 these words came to me when I was thinking about how loving, faithful and generous God is, in giving himself to those who trust Him.

I may approach Him with open hands, but He comes to me with open arms. I walk towards Him but He runs to me. God longs to give so much more to us, not just for our benefit but to enable us to be a blessing to others.

King Jesus

(2002) This song reminds us that as we follow God; He calls us His friends and we can call Him Father but He is also King.

He is the great King above all gods. (Psalm 95:3) The chorus is a prayer asking Jesus to come and reign deep in our heart and allowing Him to be Sovereign in all our ways.

When God has His rightful place in our lives, we will know His strength and rest in His provision. "For God is the King of all the earth; sing to Him a psalm of praise." (Psalm 47:7)

The puzzle "Jig"

(2001) I was asked to write a song for a Children's Holiday Club. The theme of the week was called "The Missing Piece."

Just like a jig-saw, life can be a puzzle; but when we turn to God and seek Him, He puts all the pieces together. Inside each of us; there is a "God shaped" hole that only Jesus can fill. We may try and fill that void with many things to please ourselves, but true satisfaction and contentment comes when we live life God's way.

(I still recall the "joyful jigging" as the children sang and danced to the catchy sound of the piano accordion and guitar.)

What would Jesus do? (WWJD)

(2000) Many people wear the bracelet with WWJD on it; to remind them that when decisions and questions arise, to ask – "What would Jesus do?"

Jesus would do what He says in His Word. As we read the Bible, God directs us to what is right, leads us to the truth and strengthens and helps us as we seek to obey and put into "action" what we read.

Jesus said "Whoever has my commands and obeys them, he is the one who loves me. He who loves me will be loved by my Father, and I too will love him and show myself to him." (John 14:21)

I know a King who can

(2002) A well known car breakdown service had an advert that showed a father trying to fix a car. His children ask "can you fix it?" He replies, "not this time – but I know a man who can." He then calls for his roadside mechanic.

When we need help Jesus is always there for us – the King who can do all things. Paul the apostle said "My God will meet all your needs according to His glorious riches in Christ Jesus." (Philippians 4:19)

Follow Me

This was one of my earlier songs (I didn't date my songs when I first started writing) where I endeavoured to tell a story from scripture in song. "Follow me" – comes from Matthew 4:18-22, when Jesus called His first disciples.

The second verse builds on the theme and speaks of the urgency required, to respond to the call of Jesus upon our lives. There is a cost to consider in being a disciple but Jesus gave us His all – in giving His life to forgive our sinfulness. He enables us to stand before God without guilt or shame.

Following Jesus is the way to purpose and blessing in our life on earth and the hope of heaven to come!

Baptise me

I was baptised in June 1977 at a Church Fellowship in South Chard, Somerset but I wrote this song in 2001 and shared it at the baptism service of a close friend.

The Great Commission that Jesus gave to His disciples was to "Go and make disciples of all nations, baptising them in the name of the Father, Son, and Holy Spirit and teaching them to obey everything I have commanded you. (Matthew 28:19-20)

Faithful God

(1997) This song combines words of praise and prayers, acknowledging the faithfulness of God who is faithful in all He does." (Psalm 33:4) and "…faithful to all His promises…" (Psalm 145:13b)

The chorus recognises that we need God to "move us on" in our walk with Him, as we continue to be challenged and changed by His word, and we need Him to "move us out" to the people and places; where we can share His love, faithfulness and compassion.

We are called to be faithful to our Faithful God!

In our midst

This is a prayer song to God; inviting and desiring His Spirit, to be in the middle of all we do. Jesus said, "For where two or three are gathered together in my name, I am there in the midst of them."(Matthew 18:20 NJKV)

The two lines of the chorus are easy to remember. On several occasions I would lead on the verses and get the congregation to come in on the chorus.

I have found this is a good way of teaching new songs – using a combination of listening, but also participation.

Strong love

(1995) Over the years I have had the privilege of writing and singing songs for friends, on the occasion of their wedding. God's strong love and arms will hold us firm, as we look to Him each day of our lives.

I played this song with the band "Known Aim" in the presence of Reg Varney (actor in the TV series *On The Buses*). We sang it at his daughter's wedding.

In marriage; a husband and wife love and serve one another. In our lives, we are called to love God, and out of our love for Him we serve Him and others.

The Holy Highway

(1995) This is my version of Isaiah 35 in song. I mentioned Jackie from our band in the introduction to the song "Only You."

When she was going through much suffering in her body, a friend shared these verses from Isaiah with her. Such hope! – that those who walk the Holy Highway with God here on earth, will come to the city of the Lord where there is no sorrow, no pain, no grief, sighing or tears.

In trusting in God alone, "Death has been swallowed up in victory." (1 Corinthians 15:54b)

With all your heart
(1995) This song looks at two miracles that Jesus performed, turning water into wine at a wedding in Cana and the feeding of the 5000.

The theme of the song is all about obedience. When we obey what God tells us to do, it sets the scene for a miracle to take place. We need to obey without delay!

We are to love and serve God with all our heart. "Whatever your hand finds to do – do it with all your might" (Ecclesiastes 9:10)

Where can I go?
(1990) Psalm 139 is one of my favourite scriptures. It reveals how God knows absolutely everything about us and how He is constantly thinking about us.

The chorus asks the question "Where can I go from your Spirit and presence Lord?" (Psalm 139:7) The answer is simple.

There is nowhere we can go, where the Spirit of the Lord is not present. God hems us in, behind and before and lays His hand upon us. (Psalm 139:5)

Think (upon these things)

(2004) The words we speak, the feelings we have and the actions we take will all be affected by the thoughts that we allow to run through our minds each day.

The chorus (Philippians 4:8) tells us of 8 things we should focus our thoughts on.

Worry comes from a negative thought that we keep thinking about. Peace comes, as we meditate on a God-thought from His Word. "For God has not given us a spirit of fear, but of power and of love and of a sound mind." (2 Timothy 1:7)

Light on the horizon

Just as the sun is behind every dark cloud, God's strength, peace and presence is with us, through every storm of life as we look to Him. God uses every situation in our lives to teach us something. Not one experience is wasted. We can face each day with hope, confidence and assurance, knowing that God has a greater purpose for us in everything. "For my thoughts are not your thoughts, neither are your ways my ways," declares the Lord. (Isaiah 55:8)

Composed in the 80's, I recall playing this song on some occasions, with backing from a drum machine. (I had to practice carefully to keep pace with it!)

For You O Lord

(1999) These words are based on Psalm 116. God is our strong Deliverer. He hears us, when we call on His Name.

For this book I have selected a balance in my songs, where we thank God for all He has done for us, but most importantly that we praise and worship Him for Who He is! God is righteous, compassionate, gracious and good.

God is worthy of our praise all the time. "Give thanks in all circumstances, for this is God's will for you in Christ Jesus." (1 Thessalonians 5:18)

Thorn in the hay

I have always found it a challenge to write a Christmas song that retains the real meaning and truth of Jesus coming to earth and trying to express it in a new way.

I used "poetic licence" in this song; when I had a thought – that in the hay of the stable where Jesus was born, there could well have been thorns on bramble branches.

The thorn reminds us of the crown of thorns that was placed on the head of Jesus when He was crucified – to take away the sins of the world.

Glory to God in the highest

(1990) One of the things I have done solo on occasions with my guitar playing and singing is to go into our town at Christmas and Easter and sing songs. I call these "Reason for the season" opportunities. I took a case of Bible verse booklets with me, covering various topics which people could take free of charge.

There's a story told of some young lads who were throwing stones near a Church. One stone veered off course and went through the stained glass window knocking a hole through the letter "e" of the word Highest. The text then read "Glory to God in the High st." I have shared this song a good number of times in my High Street and hope it has brought glory to God – and hope to those listening.

Fully God and Fully Man

(2009) The amazing truth of the Christmas story is that the "Word" which was with God and was God from the beginning became flesh and lived for awhile among us. In Jesus Christ we see the glory of the one and only begotten Son, who came from the Father, full of grace and truth. (John 1:1,14) Jesus was a man of sorrows and familiar with suffering – He was fully human and fully God. He can sympathize with our weaknesses, for He was tested in all points as we are, yet without sin. (See Hebrews 4:15)

To the King who reigns

(2006) These lyrics are based on Isaiah 9 and tell us that the government will be on the shoulders of Jesus – God's Son. There will be no end to the increase of His government and peace.

Whatever we see going on in the world, however chaotic and broken; whatever we may face personally – God is still in control and He reigns!

The Magi's song

(2010) This final song in the book speaks about the Magi's visit to Jesus from their perspective. They were on a journey; searching for the new born King.

They brought precious gifts to Him but most importantly, they brought worship to the King of all Kings. They sought Him and found Him!

Jesus said, "Ask and it will be given you; seek and you will find; knock and the door will be opened to you. For everyone who asks receives; he who seeks finds; and to him who knocks, the door will be opened" (Matthew 7:7-8). My hope is that the words of these songs will have a part, in you seeking, finding and knowing Jesus as your Saviour and Friend.

God has put a new song into my heart
He has lifted me higher into His arms
Yesterday's gone – and I have a new start
And I want to praise the Lord!

Also by Jim Collins

SOMETHING TO THINK ABOUT
(52 Modern Day Parables)

Jim Collins has been a Lay preacher for over 30 years within the Torbay area of South Devon. 'Something to Think About' is a compilation of his writing for the parish page of a weekly newspaper under the heading of 'Thought for the Week'.

The items were written for a wider readership, so this book will encourage Christians in their walk with God and is an excellent resource to give to anyone to point them God-wards. Using everyday experiences, and some topical issues, Jim uses a mixture of scripture, interesting information and hints of humour to show that God is able to make himself known "in all things."

To order a copy phone 01803 858340
Email: james.p.collins@btopenworld.com